Usborne
Lots of things to Spot in
London

Written by Matthew Oldham
Illustrated by David Semple

Designed by Amy Manning,
Laura Nelson and Jodie Smith
Edited by Anna Milbourne

See where this book takes you!

Take a boat to **Tower Bridge** on pages 4-5.

Ride the bus to **Trafalgar Square** on pages 6-7.

Go shopping in **Camden Market** on pages 8-9.

Sit back and relax in **Hyde Park** on pages 10-11.

Wave to royalty at **Buckingham Palace** on pages 14-15.

Dance in the streets at the **Notting Hill Carnival** on pages 12-13.

Watch out for dragons in **Chinatown** on pages 16-17.

See the bright lights above **Piccadilly Circus** on pages 18-19.

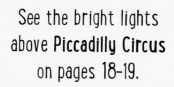

Mind the gap when you visit an **Underground station** on pages 20-21.

Hear Big Ben ring in the New Year on the **South Bank** on pages 22-23.

You'll find lots more puzzles and activities on pages 24-30 and answers on pages 31-32.

Look out for these London characters who appear in every scene...

Atticus Redfern
A fashionable fox who finds any excuse to play his violin.

Mandy Clicksqueak
A photographer mouse who sniffs out great pictures everywhere she goes.

Bill Snufflebrook
A forgetful business badger who is always running late.

Hazel Nutbury
A wealthy squirrel who travels around London in style.

Tad Croakby
A young froglet who is so excited to see the sights, his parents sometimes struggle to keep within hopping distance.

Hettie Spiker
An East-End hedgehog who takes her three grandhoglets on day trips all over the city.

Tad wants to send a postcard from each place he visits. Help him spot a red pillar box in every scene.

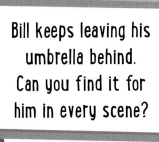

Bill keeps leaving his umbrella behind. Can you find it for him in every scene?

Trafalgar Square

We're feeding these six pigeons. Can you spot which two are exactly the same?

How many bicycles can you spot?

Camden Market

Notting Hill Carnival

Buckingham Palace

Can you spot these things?

Hat with a green feather

Royal carriage

Giraffe guard

Royal Standard flag

Who is marching behind the drummers?

How many green drums can you count?

The Queen is waving from her balcony. Can you see her?

14

Chinatown

Can you spot each of these things?

Golden
pagoda

Dragon
statue

Chinatown
arch

Yellow
lantern

How many golden
cat ornaments can
you count?

Bakery

NOODLES

KNICK-KNACKS

Fireworks for sale

open

open

Can you find
the tail part of
my costume?

Piccadilly Circus

Can you spot these things?

Zebra crossing

Eros Statue

Phone box

Stage scenery

Can you see which cake above me is the odd one out?

Which lamppost needs a new light bulb?

Underground Station

Where's the rest of our school group?

Can you find my twin brother?

TRAIN APPROACHING

London Aquarium

London Aquarium

There are five differences between these two posters. Can you spot them?

How many of each of these can you spot?

Ticket machines

Clocks

Polar bear guards

Green backpacks

Newspapers

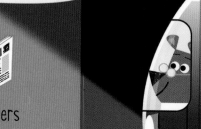

20

The South Bank

Map of London

Camden Market

Regent's Park

Notting Hill

Chinatown

Trafalgar Square

Piccadilly Circus

Hyde Park

The Houses of Parliament

Buckingham Palace

24

Regent's Canal

Use the stickers at the back of this book to fill in this map of London.

N

W   E

S

An Underground station

The Tower of London

River Thames

The South Bank

25

Getting Around

Number 11 red bus

Orange daisy bike

Look back through the book. Can you spot each of these ways of getting around in London?

Blue rickshaw

A black taxi with its yellow light on

Green paddle boat

Build a Bridge

Use the stickers at the back of this book to build Tower Bridge.

London Costume Party

My blue police helmet is so smart.

I'm dressed as the Lord Mayor.

Use the stickers at the back of this book to help each character get ready for the party.

We love the Beefeater Guards' uniforms.

With this hat, I'm tall enough to guard Buckingham Palace!

We're dressed like royalty.

All aboard! I look just like a guard on the London Underground.

I'm ready to dance at the carnival.

I could be the coolest badger in Camden Market.

Mandy's Photos

Look back through the book to find out where I've taken each picture.

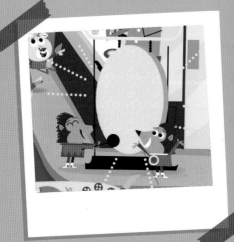

Park Maze

I'm running late for the Notting Hill Carnival! Can you show me the way through Hyde Park?

Help me fill in this picture.

Answers

4-5 Tower Bridge

- ⬤ Seven ravens
- ◯ Four life rings
- ◯ Five Beefeaters
- ◯ One crest

Differences between boats

- ⬤ Boat with eight blue oars
- ◯ The smell is coming from the chestnut seller.
- ⬤ Hazel Nutbury is passing under the bridge.
- ◯ Lord Mayor

6-7 Trafalgar Square

- ⬤ Portrait painter
- ◯ Nelson's Column
- ◯ Red gallery banner
- ◯ Tour guide

- ◯ Lost police helmet
- ◯ Matching pigeons
- ◯ There are eight bicycles.
- ◯ The number 11 bus has the most passengers.
- ⬤ The number 9 bus is here.

8-9 Camden Market

- ⬤ Star glasses stall
- ⬤ Knitted hats stall
- ◯ Basket bag stall
- ◯ Tie-dyed T-shirt stall

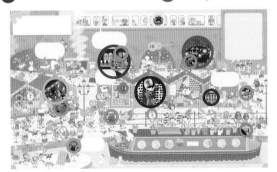

- ◯ Lost bag
- ◯ Boot without a pair
- ◯ Seven blue wigs
- ◯ The spider has bought something from the music stall.
- ⬤ Yes, there are enough cakes for everyone waiting in line.

10-11 Hyde Park

- ⬤ Nine pink ice creams
- ⬤ Six deck chairs
- ◯ Five red skateboards
- ◯ Four picnic baskets

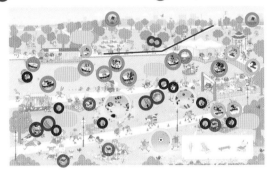

- ◯ Matching kites
- ◯ Empty table at the café
- ◯ There are eight blue boats.
- ◯ Three ball games
- ⌒ The way to the park gates is marked in red.

12-13 Notting Hill Carnival

- ⬤ Two blue flower dancers
- ⬤ Seven steel drums
- ◯ Three stilt walkers
- ◯ Eight maracas

- ◯ Dancing policeman
- ◯ Nine red flags
- ◯ Matching dancing partner
- ⬤ Mandy Clicksqueak is throwing confetti.
- ◯ The orange balloon belongs to Tad Croakby.
- ◯ Pineapple drinks on sale here

14-15 Buckingham Palace

- ⬤ Hat with a green feather
- ◯ Royal carriage
- ◯ Giraffe guard
- ◯ Royal Standard flag

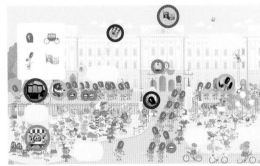

- ◯ Four green drums
- ◯ The Queen
- ◯ Flags on sale here
- ⬤ Castle balloon
- ◯ Pink cloth
- ◯ Atticus Redfern is behind the drummers.

16-17 Chinatown

- ◉ Golden pagoda
- ◉ Dragon statue
- ○ Chinatown arch
- ○ Yellow lantern

- ○ Costume tail
- ○ Fireworks on sale here
- ◉ There are nine golden cat ornaments.
- ○ Umbrella with the most green spots
- ○ Bill Snufflebrook has left the trail of rice.

18-19 Piccadilly Circus

- ◉ Zebra crossing
- ◉ Eros statue
- ○ Phone box
- ○ Stage scenery

- ○ This cake is the odd one out.
- ○ Hettie Spiker and her grandhoglets are on the top floor of the bus.
- ◉ This lamppost needs a new light bulb.
- ○ Three lost play tickets
- ○ Five Nutcracker booklets

20-21 Underground Station

- ◉ Three ticket machines
- ◉ Two clocks
- ○ Four polar bear guards
- ○ Eight green backpacks

Differences between the posters

- ◉ Nine newspapers
- ○ Twin brother bear
- ○ The school group is here.
- ◉ There are six passengers wearing hats on the train.
- ○ Flowers on sale here

22-23 South Bank

- ◉ London Eye
- ○ Pink feather boa
- ○ Glitter ball
- ○ Heart-shaped firework
- ○ Clock

- ○ Drinks on sale here
- ○ Tad Croakby is at the front of the conga line.
- ◉ Dropped blue gloves
- ○ Costume party
- ○ Ten party hats

Getting Around

- Number 11 bus: page 7
- Blue rickshaw: page 16
- Black taxi with yellow light: page 19
- Orange daisy bike: page 15
- Green paddle boat: page 10

London Costume Party

Build a Bridge

Mandy's Photos

Page 22 Page 18 Page 10 Page 15 Page 12

Page 21 Page 9 Page 4 Page 6 Page 17

Park Maze

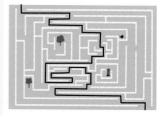

This is the way through Hyde Park.

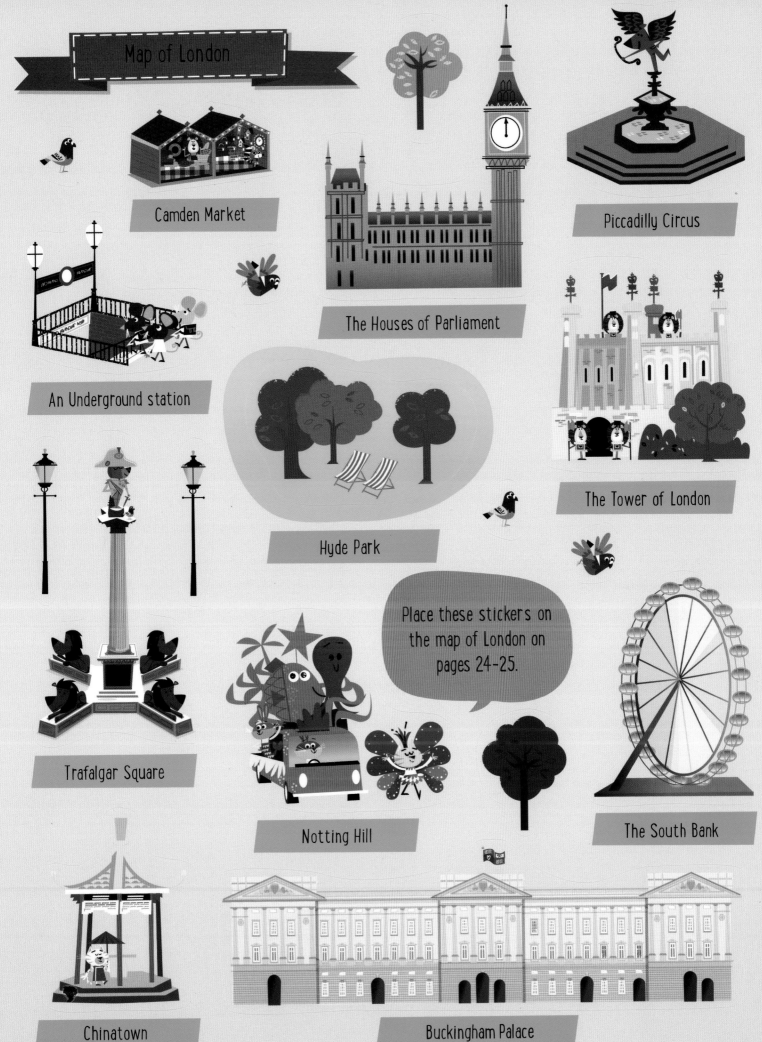

Map of London

Camden Market

The Houses of Parliament

Piccadilly Circus

An Underground station

The Tower of London

Hyde Park

Trafalgar Square

Place these stickers on the map of London on pages 24-25.

Notting Hill

The South Bank

Chinatown

Buckingham Palace

Use these stickers to decorate the map of London on pages 24-25.

Put these trees in the parks and green spaces.

Stick these boats on the river, or the canal.

These stickers can go anywhere along the streets.

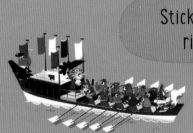
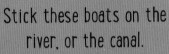

Unscramble these stickers to rebuild Tower Bridge on page 26.

Use these stickers to dress each character for the London costume party on page 27.

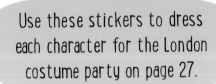

Here are more stickers for the London costume party on page 27.

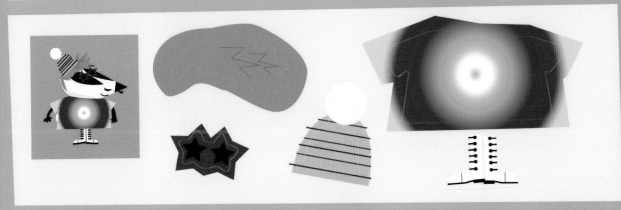

You can use these stickers wherever you like.

Stick these under the photos on page 28 after you've spotted where Mandy has taken each picture.